smells

insulting!

Oonagh

horrible

the Scottish Giant

His shield, mace,

cut off

Benandonner

hammer, 13 knives

cross sea

the Biggest, Roughest, Toughest Street - Fighting Giant in all of Scotland!

helmet and enormous

two handed sword

This book is dedicated to~ Cyril. S. Hall. Architect, father and friend.

Cheers Dad.

with special thanks to Mr. Frank Holden.

There is a rumour abroad that Daniel Ferguson and Stephen Hall are, in fact, the same person. This is true. I originally wrote my version of this Finn tale under a pen name, borrowed from my maternal grand father, the original Daniel Ferguson. He was a train driver, based at Coleraine and he drove the Portrush Flyer, (but that's another story). This was my way of paying my respects to my roots and the sound of the voices that I listened to as a wee man visiting the houses and farms of relations with names like McBride, Robinson and Kirkpatrick. We are all influenced by what we are told and what we hear, when we are young.

It shapes how we see the the world around us.

Thanks also to my "wee mammy " Frances and my aunts, Ruby, Eva, Mollie and Aideen. They have all helped and influenced me along the way.

x x o o

THE GIANT'S CAUSEWAY.

RETOLD BY

Daniel Ferguson
~Designed & illustrated by
Stephen Hall.

Republished by Earth Native Art, third edition. ISBN 0-9528922-0-0
Tel: 02893 378583. *(or international calls: +44 2893 378583.)*
Website: www.earthnativeart.co.uk or e.mail: theweebear@hotmail.com.
Hand scripted in Celto - Gaelic "Spoof" medium. Copyright Stephen Hall. First published in July 1996. We hope you enjoy the read.

To contact The Giants Causeway Visitors Centre Tel: +44 28 207 31855.

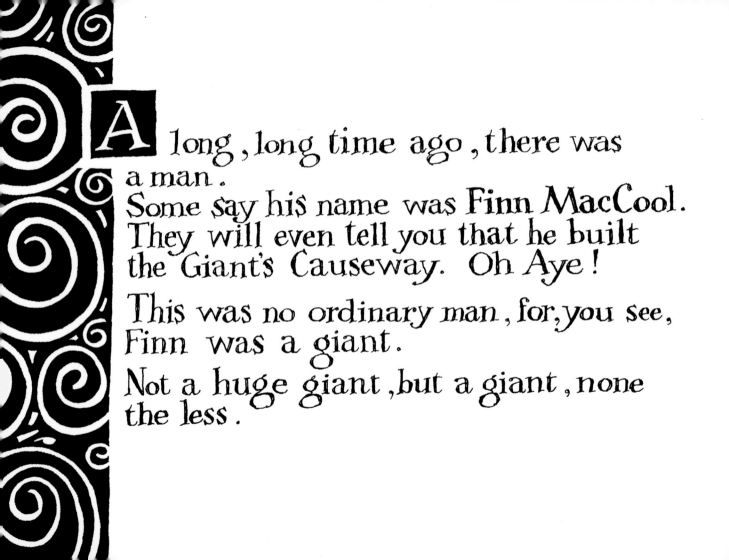

A long, long time ago, there was a man.
Some say his name was Finn MacCool.
They will even tell you that he built the Giant's Causeway. Oh Aye!

This was no ordinary man, for, you see, Finn was a giant.

Not a huge giant, but a giant, none the less.

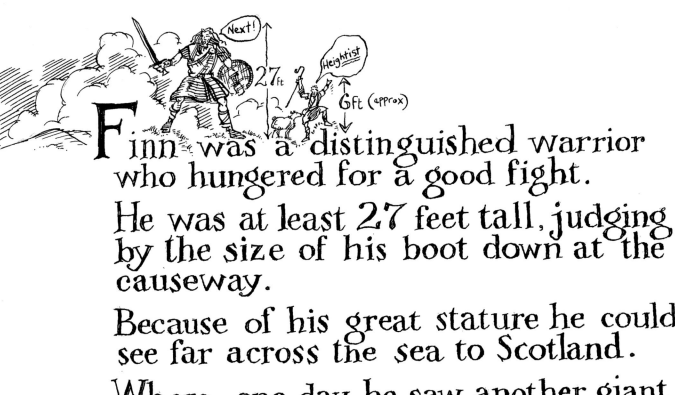

Finn was a distinguished warrior who hungered for a good fight.

He was at least 27 feet tall, judging by the size of his boot down at the causeway.

Because of his great stature he could see far across the sea to Scotland.

Where, one day he saw another giant. "Hey you!" he called out to the distant massive shape.

"You smell like rotten fish. Do you never wash, man dear?"

Benandonner, the Scottish giant heard the voice from across the sea and turned, out of casual curiosity, to listen to what the wee Irish giant was ranting about.

"Your breath smells horrible, like cow dung on a hot day. You Big Ejit!" shouted Finn.

The giant listened. He could hardly believe his ears. Who was this impetuous FOOL?

Did this wee man not know who he was insulting?

The Biggest, Roughest, Toughest Street-Fighting Giant in all of Scotland!

ONE GAUNTLET

ONE BIG THUMPY TYPE THING

CERTIFIED MEAN

Do Not
REMOVE
FROM SHOP

Benandonner decided, then and there, that he would cut off Finn Mac Cool's head, display it on his spear outside his house and feed the rest of him to the crows!

oh dear

Nice bit of leg

It seemed only fair.

As Finn shouted more insults, Benandonner became more and more ANGRY.

A bright light crackled and shone from his bulging eyes.

His head, ears, nose and mouth started to produce billowing clouds of steam in the steady down pour of rain that persisted overhead.

windy blowelee

sssss
sizzle

ssss

He opened his Huge, Gaping, Ugly Mouth and *roared* a torrent of unrepeatable Gaelic insults at Finn MacCool.

Even the sheep and cattle were embarrassed at Benandonner's lack of social decorum.

You know. You can take these Scotsmen absolutely <u>nowhere</u>!

Benandonner reached down with his big sinewy hands, lifted and threw a cluster of huge rocks towards Finn.

Some fell, with a mighty splash into the sea and at that moment a great whale shot up into the air with a surprised expression on it's face, only to crash back down into the water. (*kersploosh!*)

PLOOP! PLOOP!

AMAZED

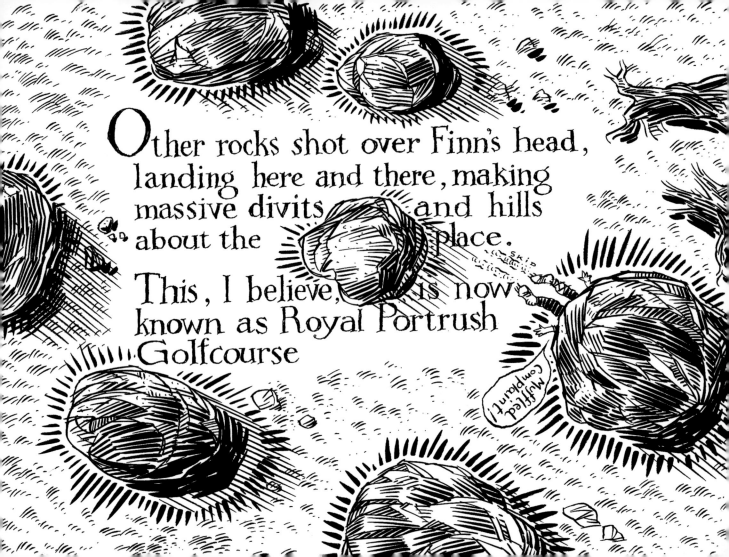

Other rocks shot over Finn's head, landing here and there, making massive divits and hills about the place.

This, I believe, is now known as Royal Portrush Golfcourse

SKIP

Muffled Complaint.

All this stone throwing,
(A traditional sport in the north of Ireland)
well it gave Finn MacCool an idea

He had a load of stones that he had
cut and shaped to make a sort of paved
area for Oonagh (*his wife*) and children
back at the house.

Now he had a much better use
for them !

Load after load of these hexagonal
shaped stones he carried in his big
strong arms down to the sea shore,
from where he began to create a
Causeway or bridge.

It would stretch from the
North Antrim coast all the way
to Scotland where his large
adversary lodged.

Oh, if only Finn had known
the true size of Benandonner
he would, most likely, have built
the Causeway towards America!

When Finn MacCool finally
laid his last stone and reached
Scotland, he called out
to Benandonner,
but there was no reply.

There was only the sound of the rain and the wind blowing through the heather.

So off he set (*faster than any sea ferry.*) back across the 18 miles of causeway to get his tea and "put his feet up," thinking no more of the Scottish

Monster

Rasp!!

The next day, Scotland was Wet....
....as usual!

Benandonner awoke. *Yawn...*

After refreshing himself with that stuff
the Scots call porridge (*we call it
cement here*) and a few lightly grilled
Highland Cattle on toast, washed
down with seven barrels of tea,
he set off for his morning stroll. *Burp!*

O nly to notice the newly constructed causeway, leading off towards the North Antrim coast and the MacCool family residence.

Enraged at the fact that no planning permission had been applied for, Benandonner quickly returned home to pick up his tools of the trade.

PLANNING PERMISSION

Any silly
Wee Irish
Giants wanting
to build any
stupid little
CAUSEWAYS
Should "Give
me the
NOD!
~RIGHT?

His shield, mace, hammer,
13 (*individually named*) knives,
battle helmet, armour and an
ENORMOUS
two handed sword called ~

MacSLICER (*SWOOSH!*).
GAAATHUGG.

Benandonner then stomped off
to discuss the matter with
the young MacCool.

I'm really Angry

RaGinG StoRm

The ground shook, the sea *tore itself* into a and Finns finely jointed causeway RATTLED under the immense weight of the dark ominous shape approaching from Scotland.

CLINK!

Ben's Abode

Finn's Place

By chance Finn's wife, Oonagh, was just hanging out the washing when she heard, what she thought, was distant thunder, coming from the direction of Scotland.

As she stared out to sea she began to make out the **ENORMOUS!** shape of Benandonner approaching.

Through the mists he came.
Across the sea and storms he came.
Over THE GIANT'S CAUSEWAY
he came to have a battle,
to the death,
with

FINN MacCOOL!

Oonagh gave warning to Finn!
who could not believe his eyes.
("Mmmmmm, _he's a bit of a ~Big Lad!_") -thought Finn

This giant was B·I·G.

I don't just mean "big".....as in.....
"_Big Savings!_, _Big Deal!_, or _Big Head!_"

No!

I mean . . . .

Italian

BIGAMISSIMO!

German

BIGGERRSTAMPEN!

Scandanavian

SkuLLdecrushhindoo!

Dutch

Hittenwreckinflotten

American

HUGE

Hi.

Japanese

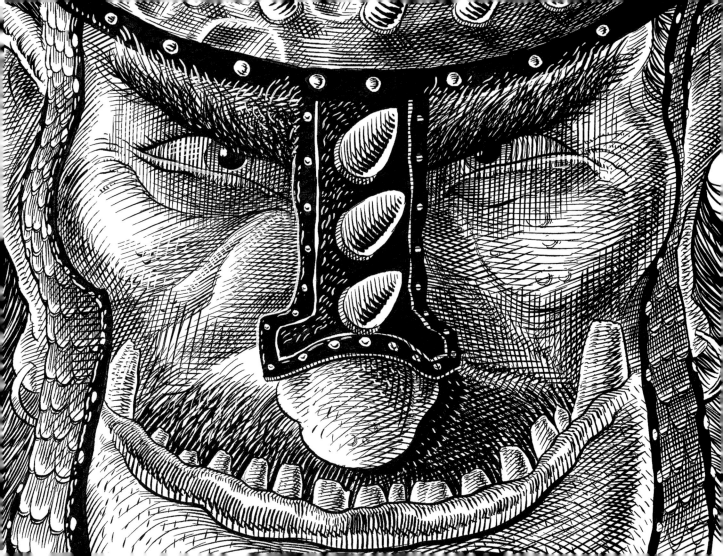

Yes,..I mean....**"Oh Mommie!** where am I going to hide? **"Big"**

You see the distance across the sea, had tricked Finn into thinking that BENANDONNER (*that nice wee Scottish ~ stone-heaver*) was only about his size.

(*He could feel a severe beating coming on. Until........*)

He spied his youngest child asleep in his cot. (aaaWWWWWw.) *SYMPATHETIC*

Oonagh, with great haste, reached for her wash basket and Finn pulled up his coracle. Together they made a "do it yourself" cradle.

Into which, jumped Finn, disguising himself as a

BIG BABY.

MHHHHH Shakey! Shakey Gurgle Gurgle

CLANG!

SNAP!

ACTION BEN

A B C

J ust in time too,
for Oonagh had only
tucked Finn into the cradle
"*Snug as a bug in a rug*"
when the Scottish giant
came STRIDING
up the hill towards
the MacCool house.

Time to graze
on the lower pasture
dear

A larger breed
of sheep. Now
EXTINCT.

I'm here, for the Head of that weeeeee GIANT, Finn MacCool. Where is he?
Who me?

oh pooooo!

Oonagh calmly stepped out from under the giant's shadow, into the light of day and answered Benandonner.

"Finn has gone out for a wee jog this morning. He normally does 20 laps of Ireland, before lunchtime. Would you like to stay and have a bite to eat with us? Finn's partial to a bit of Scottish Beef."

"Sit yourself down and have a cup of tea. Sure isn't the potato bread, just this minute off the griddle!"

So the great giant pulled up a chair and sat down to have a cup of tea with Oonagh.

Mummy!

Conversation was limited
to the weather and the *finer* points
of causeway construction.
Punctuated only by long silences,
when all you could hear
was the sound of the sea,
the delicate plinking of tea cups
with saucer, the sound of the gulls
and the odd
sssss *sllURping*
Aahhhhhh
of tea!

After a time, Benandonner noticed
the large cradle that Oonagh
would occasionally take a peak
into, and gently rock.

"What's in that big basket?" he asked,
getting up from his seat to take
a closer *look*.

Goo Goo, Gurgle, Fo Fo, Do Do

Ta for the Tattie Bread
— Lassie.

wheeeeek

SMASH!

Tinkle.

"Why that's our youngest."
replied Oonagh, with a twinkle
in her eye.
"Would you like to see him?"

"Your..... What?" said the giant,
spitting tea and lumps of potato bread
all down his front. (very Messy)

"Oh yes." said Oonagh
This is Oisin "

PRONOUNCED LIKE 'WASHIN' EXCEPT WITH AN "O"
INSTEAD OF A "W".

" He's only 7 months old
and such a fine head of hair already!

If you think Oisin's BIG.....

You should see his

FATHER "

The Scottish giant was a bit
"taken-a-back".

In fact he went into

DEEP SHOCK

A paralysing fear
overtook him as adrenalin
pumped through his veins.

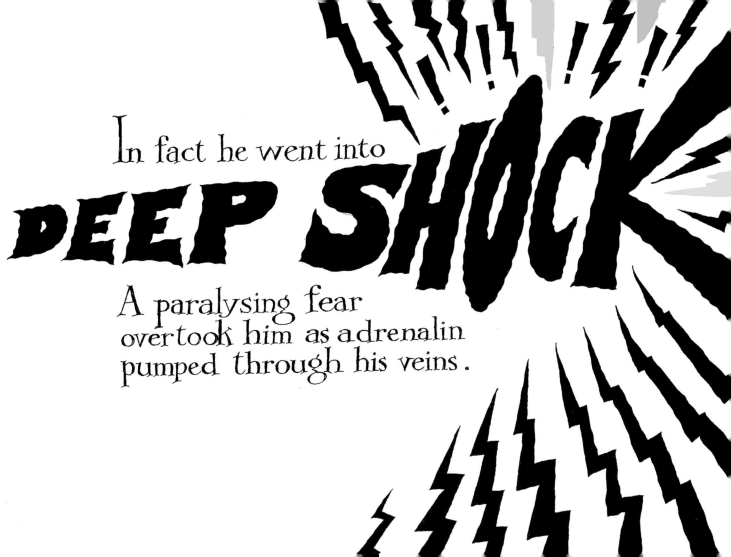

His **hair**
almost left his head.
turning a *Snowy White*
on either temple making him look like
an ENORMOUS
PUNK, Badger, Traffic-Warden!

* 'Temple' means the side of YER head!

He lost a lot of weight
very, very quickly,
but good taste prevents me
from describing the scene,
when Benandonner
scaled up in his mind
Just how
BIG....

Big Huge Gigantic ENORMOUS

Needless to say Benandonner
didn't hang about.
He politely made his excuses ~
something about judging
a HIGHland cattle

Whooooo ffff!

THROWING COMPETITION

Just for a second I actually thought that you wir gonning

at Ayr, and left.
"Legging it for home."

Thanks for having me
SADLY even at his lighter fighting weight, Benandonner still managed to WRECK the already SHAKEN causeway, leaving only what you see here today.
Mac Knackered!

Finn, Oonagh and the children
lived for "manys a year after".
Many tales have been told
of this **GIANT** among men.

We will never really know
if these stories are just stories,
or if a warrior called Finn MacCool
really existed.

Many folk believe he did exist.

PERHAPS A SLIGHTLY SMALLER VERSION?

Yer Mum & I with the children
Moyle Sea Beach. 210 A.D.